WINK

by Phoebe Eclair-Powell

WINK was first produced by Tara Finney Productions and Theatre503,
receiving its world premiere at Theatre503, London,
on 10 March 2015

WINK

by Phoebe Eclair-Powell

CAST

John	Leon Williams
Mark	Sam Clemmett

CREATIVE TEAM

Director	Jamie Jackson
Designer	Bethany Wells
Lighting Designer	Aaron J. Dootson
Sound Designer	Max Pappenheim
Movement Director	Isla Jackson-Ritchie
Dramaturg	Graeme Thompson
Casting Director	Tara Finney
Graphic Designer	Adam Loxley
Design Assistant	Freyja Costelloe
Lighting Assistant	Sam Wright

PRODUCTION TEAM

Producer	Tara Finney Productions & Theatre503
Production Manager	Jamie Kluckers
Stage Manager	Lisa Cochrane
Production Assistant	Hannah Turk
Resident Assistant Producer	Franky Green
Press Representative	Chloe Nelkin Consulting

WINK would not have been possible without the support of

Arts Council England
Jenny Eclair
Susie Blake
Julia Duff
Richard Allen-Turner
June Hargreaves
Sarah Hargreaves
Alison Jackson
Jo Bourke
Margot Gavan Duffy
Benjamin Hargreaves
Grainne Marmion
Geoffrey Powell
Linda Robson
MJ Sparks
Tom Finney

Caroline Hewitt
Daniel Isaacs
Ronnie Jackson
Clive Merrison
Noelle Morris
Judith Parker
Rob Ritchie
Lizzie Roper
Graham Warrener
Agnes Baker
Alison Barnett
Steve Bennett
Rebecca Bleach
Ashley Deans
Stella Duffy
Shelley Silas

Christopher George
Peter Genower
Vicky Graham
Kevin James
Helen Lederer
Jan Norman
Jennifer Pearce
Joel Phillimore
David Ralf
Karen Richards
Sue Swift
Martin Thompson
Clare Whiting
Conel Wingrave

We would also like to thank

Stage One
Old Vic New Voices
503Futures
Company of Angels
Royal Court Theatre
English Touring Theatre
National Theatre
Polka Theatre
Clapham Omnibus
Iris Theatre
Theatre Renegade
JKP Technical Production Services
MWScenery
JE Lighting Services
Concept Audio
ROSCO Lighting
LED Lighthouse
White Light

Sparks Theatrical
Sam Underwood of
Underwood Films
Alex Harvey-Brown of
Savannah Photographic
Winston's Wish
George MacKay
Tommy McDonnell
James Cooney
Jordan Mifsud
Jack McMullen
Ryan Kiggell
SJ Clarkson
Charlotte Spencer
Jordan Whitwell
Cindy Gallop of
Make Love Not Porn

BIOGRAPHIES

Leon Williams – John
Theatre credits include: *Hobson's Choice* (Regent's Park Open Air Theatre); *One Man, Two Guvnors* (UK tour with the National Theatre); *The Bullet* (Hampstead); *As You Like It* (Rose, Kingston); *A Midsummer Night's Dream* (Shakespeare's Globe).

TV credits include: *New Tricks* and *Call the Midwife* (both BBC One).

Sam Clemmett – Mark
Theatre credits include: *Accolade* (St James); *Nivelli's War* (Northern Ireland tour); *Lord of the Flies* (Regent's Park Open Air Theatre).

TV credits include: *Diary of a Snob* (lead, Nickelodeon Pilot), *Foyle's War, Holby City, Doctors.*

Film credits include: *Survivor*.

Phoebe Eclair-Powell – Writer

Phoebe is a writer from South East London, *WINK* is her first full-length debut. She is currently on the Soho Writers Lab and on the Channel 4 Screenwriting course for 2014/15. Phoebe is represented by Ikenna Obiekwe at Independent Talent.

Theatre credits include: *One Under* (Pleasance Below); *Mrs Spine* (OUTLINES at the Old Red Lion); *Bangin' Wolves* (Courting Drama at the Bush Upstairs, published by Playdead Press, later with Polaroid Theatre for Wilderness Festival); two rapid write response pieces, *Coal Eaters* and *Glass Hands* (Theatre503); *The Box* (Theatre Delicatessen SPACED festival and Latitude Festival); *Elephant and My Castle* (SALT Theatre at Southwark Playhouse); *CARE* (Miniaturists at the Arcola).

Film credits include: script support for Bella Films on upcoming film *Cover Girl*.

Jamie Jackson – Director

Theatre credits include: *SKINT* (Vaults Festival); *The View From Down Here* (Ovalhouse); *Alice Through the Looking Glass* (St Paul's Church); *Life on a Plum* (Nabokov/Polaroid/Wilderness Festival); *London Boys* (Greenwich). Jamie has also directed *CARE* (Arcola); *Coal Eaters* (Theatre503); *Bangin' Wolves* (Bush Attic/ Wilderness Festival) all by Phoebe Eclair-Powell.

As Assistant Director: *The El Train* (Hoxton Hall) and *The Act* (Trafalgar Studios).

Bethany Wells – Designer

Bethany is a performance and interaction designer, working across dance, theatre and installation. Trained in architecture at the Bartlett School of Architecture and the Royal College of Art, she has been awarded a 110 Anniversary Scholarship at the University of Leeds for PhD research into performance design.

Performance credits include: *There, There Stranger* (John Ross Dance, Sadler's Wells); *Trois Ruptures* (Chelsea); *All I Want* (Kirsty Housley, Jackson's Lane); *Disnatured* (Simmer Dim, RIFT/New Diorama); *The Immortal Hour* (Tarquin Productions, Finborough); *Impossible Lecture* (Indivisible, Beacons Festival); *17* (Finborough); *Canterbury Tales* (Impulse Collective, New Diorama); *Spokesong* (Simmer Dim, Finborough); *It Burns It All Clean* (Selina Thompson, West Yorkshire Playhouse).

Work in development includes: *The Unfair* (Ellie Harrison, Theatre in the Mill) and *WARMTH*, a wood-fired mobile sauna and experimental performance space.

Aaron J. Dootson – Lighting Designer
Aaron trained at Wimbledon College of Art with a distinction in Lighting Design and Practice.

Theatre credits include: *Singin' in the Rain, The Blonde Bombshells of 1943, Romeo and Juliet, Avenue Q* (Upstairs at the Gatehouse); *Long Story Short* and *Ushers* (Charing Cross); *The Last 5 Years* (The King's Arms, Salford); *I Could've Been Better* (Pleasance, Edinburgh); *Romeo and Juliet, Twelfth Night* (Theatre Royal, Northampton); *The Bullet and the Bass Trombone, Only Us* (Bristol Old Vic Studio); *Actéon* (Dartington Summer School); *Green Forms* (Tabard); *Love Thy Neighbour, Bluebird* (Cockpit); *Dido and Aeneas* (Barn Theatre); *74 Georgia Avenue* (New End); *After the Accident* (Soho); *This Is How It Goes* (King's Head).

As Associate Lighting Designer: *Jacques Brel, Lost Boys* (Charing Cross Theatre – Lighting Designer, Mike Robertson).

Relights include: *The Perfect Murder* (UK tour – Lighting Designer, Mark Howett) and *Private Peaceful* (UK tour 2011 – Lighting Designer, Wayne Dowdeswell).

Max Pappenheim – Sound Designer
Nominated for OffWestEnd Awards 2012 and 2014 for Best Sound Designer.

Theatre credits include: *Toast, The Man Who Shot Liberty Valance, Archimedes' Principle* (Park); *CommonWealth* (Almeida); *Little Light, The Distance* (Orange Tree, Richmond); *Ghost, Strangers on a Train* (English Theatre, Frankfurt); *Usagi Yojimbo, Johnny Got His Gun, Three Sisters, Fiji Land, Our Ajax* (Southwark Playhouse); *Mrs Lowry and Son* (Trafalgar Studios); *Coolatully, Rachel, Martine, Variation on a Theme, Black Jesus, Somersaults, The Fear of Breathing* (Finborough); *The Faction's Rep Season 2015* (New Diorama); *The Armour, The Hotel Plays* (Defibrillator at the Langham Hotel); *Giovanni* (Silent Opera); *Being Tommy Cooper* (national tour); *Shipwrecked!, Irma Vep, Kafka v Kafka* (Brockley Jack); *Freefall* (New Wimbledon Studio); *Awkward Conversations with Animals I've F*cked* (Underbelly, Edinburgh); *Below the Belt* (Pleasance, Edinburgh).

As Associate Sound Designer: *The Island* (Young Vic); *Fleabag* (Soho).

Isla Jackson-Ritchie – Movement Director
Isla is a freelance movement director currently working alongside choreographer Siobhan Davis in a choreographic training programme.

Theatre credits include: *Coal Eaters* (Theatre503); *Alice Through the Looking Glass* (St Paul's Church); *This Is Your Life* (Wilderness Festival); *Tell Me a Secret* (Airborne Theatre Edinburgh Fringe Festival); *Into the Dark* (Stage at Leeds); *SKINT* (Vaults Festival, Old Vic Tunnels).

Graeme Thompson – Dramaturg
Graeme is Creative Producer at Live Theatre in Newcastle as well as a freelance producer and dramaturg. His role at Live is to coordinate the theatre's main-house productions as well as develop commissions, touring and co-productions. He was previously Literary Coordinator at Theatre503 and has worked for various other organisations including the West Yorkshire Playhouse.

Freyja Costelloe – Design Assistant
Freyja trained in Theatre Arts and Performance Design at Middlesex University. She has been involved in designing a range of productions from outdoor work to fringe to the West End. Her interest in theatre design arises from the desire to create a visual language; one that is transformative and engaged with constant evolution and opportunity. With a keen interest in new writing and collaborative processes, she is constantly investigating the relationship of changing space and art within performance design.

Theatre credits include: *Gods and Monsters* (Design Assistant, Southwark Playhouse); *Happy Birthday Without You* (Designer, Tricycle Theatre); *Scene and Heard* (Costume Designer/Maker, Theatro Technis); *This Is Where We're From* (Designer, Clean Break); *Chickenshed – Young Creators* (Designer/ Facilitator, Ravensfield Theatre); *The Dreams of Sleeping Beauty* (Minack); *The Marriage of Figaro* (Design Assistant, Upstairs at the Gatehouse); *Grease* (Design Assistant, Ljublijana Festival); *Whistle Down the Wind* (Scenic Painter, Rose, Kingston).

Jamie Kluckers – Production Manager
Jamie trained in Technical Production at Guildford School of Acting and has been working in the theatre industry as a production manager, technical manager and stage manager for the past ten years. His company, JKP Technical Production Services provides production and technical support for various high-profile clients, drama schools and colleges.

Theatre credits include: *Chekhov Season – Uncle Vanya/Three Sisters* (Wyndham's); *Henry IV, V, VI* (*Wars of the Roses*), *Legally Blonde, Twang, Memory of Water* (GSA); *Guys and Dolls, Gypsy* (Chichester Festival Theatre).

Lisa Cochrane – Stage Manager
Lisa is a freelance stage manager based in London. Originally from Northern Ireland, Lisa found her way across the Irish Sea and completed her drama school training in Professional Production Skills at Guildford School of Acting.

Theatre credits include: DSM, *Sleeping Beauty* (B'pool Grand); SM on Book, *Land of Our Fathers* (Trafalgar Studios); SM show cover, *Richard III* (St Paul's Church); DSM, *King Lear* (Cockpit); SM on Book, *Flesh&Blood Women* (Baby Grand Belfast/tour); PM, *The Kitchen, the Bedroom, and the Grave* (Baby Grand/tour).

Hannah Turk – Production Assistant
Hannah works as Creative Producer for new, immersive theatre company, Dogs of War Theatre. She is working towards a Gold Arts Award with the Almeida Theatre on their Creative Board, creating and producing opportunities and events for young people in theatre. Hannah also works as Office Administrator at Iris Theatre and Workshop Assistant with Almeida Academy.

Theatre credits include: *Not What I Am, The Stanley Halls Invention Theatre Project* (Dogs of War Theatre); *YFA Scratch Night* (Almeida).

Tara Finney Productions Ltd

Tara set up Tara Finney Productions in 2013, to produce the critically acclaimed *Land of Our Fathers* (Time Out's *Fringe Show of the Year 2013*), which transferred to Trafalgar Studios in September 2014 and is set for a national tour in autumn 2015. She received a Stage One Bursary in 2014 and Tara Finney Productions Ltd was born in December 2014. *WINK* is her second independent production.

Tara qualified as a corporate solicitor before starting her theatrical career as Resident Assistant Producer at Theatre503. She then moved to Iris Theatre, leading on two open-air summer seasons in the grounds of St Paul's Church, Covent Garden. She currently works as Associate Producer at Company of Angels where she is line producing *Theatre Cafe Festival*, their flagship, pan-European festival of play readings, and *World Factory*, a co-production with Metis Arts, New Wolsey Theatre and the Young Vic.

Tara also works as a freelance casting director.

For Tara Finney Productions:
WINK (Theatre503)
Land of Our Fathers (Trafalgar Studios, Theatre503)

Other theatre credits include:
Helver's Night (York Theatre Royal)
Alice through the Looking Glass, Richard III (St Paul's Church)
Respect, Buy Nothing Day (ALRA Studio)
I, Peaseblossom / I, Caliban (national tour)
Theatre Cafe York (York Theatre Royal)
Alice in Wonderland, Julius Caesar (St Paul's Church)
Desolate Heaven, Where the Mangrove Grows, ELEGY, Life for Beginners
(Theatre503)
Bluebird (Bedlam, Courtyard, South Hill Park)

Casting credits include:
Helver's Night (York Theatre Royal)
Land of Our Fathers (Trafalgar Studios, Theatre503)
Mucky Kid (Theatre503)
The Life of Stuff (Theatre503)

Award nominations include:
Land of Our Fathers – Best New Play, Best Production (FINALIST), Best Director, Best Set Designer, Best Lighting Designer (Off West End Awards, 2014)
The Life of Stuff – Best Ensemble (Off West End Awards, 2014)

tarafinney.com | @tara_finney | facebook.com/tarafinneyproductions

Theatre503 is the award-winning home of groundbreaking plays.

Led by Artistic Director Paul Robinson, Theatre503 is a flagship fringe venue committed to producing new work that is game-changing, relevant, surprising, mischievous, visually thrilling and theatrical. Our theatre is one of London's few destinations for new writing and we offer more opportunities to new writers than any other theatre in the country.

THEATRE503 TEAM

Artistic Director	Paul Robinson
Executive Director	Jeremy Woodhouse
Producer and Head of Marketing	Polly Ingham
Associate Artistic Director	Lisa Cagnacci
Office Manager	Joe Brown
Literary Manager	Steve Harper
Literary Coordinators	Lauretta Barrow, Tom Latter
Literary Associate	Karis Halsall
Resident Assistant Producers	Franky Green, Liam Harrison
Volunteer Coordinators	Serafina Cusack, Simon Mander
'Young Creative Leaders' Project Manager	Louise Abbots
Senior Readers	Kate Brower, Clare O'Hara, Jimmy Osbourne, Imogen Sarre
Associate Directors	Gemma Fairlie, Tom Littler

THEATRE503 BOARD

Erica Whyman (Chair), Dennis Kelly, Royce Bell, Peter Benson, Chris Campbell, Kay Ellen Consolver, Ben Hall, Marcus Markou, Geraldine Sharpe-Newton, Jack Tilbury, Eleanor Lloyd, Roy Williams

And we couldn't do what we do without our brilliant volunteers:

Annabel Pemberton, Nuno Faisca, Rosie Akerman, Diyan Zora, Tobias Chapple, Joseph Ackerman, Alexandra Coyne, Anuska Zaremba-Pike, Cecilia Segar, Valeria Bello, Larner Taylor, Damian Robertson, Jumoke, Valeria Carboni, Mike Bale, Serafina Cusack, Lousie Fairbrother, Caroline Jowett, Jim Mannering, Oluwafuntu Ojumu, Imogen Robertson, Chidimma Chukwu, Jill Segal, Elena Valentine, Tess Hardy, Kenneth Hawes, Anna Gorajek, Maya Kirtley.

Theatre503 is supported by:

Angela Hyde-Courtney and the Audience Club, Kay Ellen Consolver, Cas Donald, Edna Kissman, Eileen Glynn, Deborah Shaw and Steve Marqhardt, Marisa Drew, Jerwood/Posonby, Andrew and Julia Johnson, Georgia Oetker, Stuart Mullins, Michael Morfey, Geraldine Sharpe-Newton, Penny Egan, Liz Padmore, Bernice Chitnis, Lisa Forrell, Abigail Thaw, Charlotte Westenra, Frankie Sangwin, Mike and Hilary Tyler, Sue and Keith Hamilton, Sandra Chalmers, David Chapman and Judy Molloy, Georgie Grant Haworth, Amy Rotherham, Kate Beswick, Craig Simpson, Jason Meiniger, Yve Newbold, Juliana Breitenbach.

Theatre503 would particularly like to thank the ongoing generous support of Philip and Chris Carne.

Shine a light on 503...

Theatre503 receives no public subsidy as a venue and we cannot survive without the transformative support of our friends. For as little as £23 a year, you can help us remain **'Arguably the most important theatre in Britain today'** (*Guardian*).

One-off donations also make an enormous difference to the way Theatre503 is able to operate. Whether you are able to give £10 or £1000 your gift will help us continue to create work of award-winning standard.

To become a member or make a one-off donation email your interest to: info@theatre503.com, or by post to: Theatre503, The Latchmere, 503 Battersea Park Road, London, SW11 3BW.

Alternatively visit our website **theatre503.com** or ring 020 7978 7040 to sign up for membership directly.

If you are a UK tax payer and able to make a gift aid donation please let us know as we receive 25p per pound more on top of your donation in government grant.

Theatre503, 503 Battersea Park Rd, London, SW11 3BW | 020 7978 7040 | theatre503.com | @Theatre503 | Facebook.com/theatre503

WINK

Phoebe Eclair-Powell

Acknowledgements

Thanks to:

Jamie Jackson for everything.

To Isla Jackson-Ritchie, Alison Jackson, Graeme Thompson, Tara Finney, Bethany Wells, Toby Bruce, Vicky Featherstone and all at the Royal Court. To Old Vic New Voices, Paul Robinson, Steve Harper and all at Theatre503 for their continued and committed support. To the ever-there Ikenna Obiekwe. To Cicely Hadman and Katie Carpenter for all your help in infancy. To George MacKay, Tommy McDonnell and James Cooney for lighting matches. To Sam Clemmett and Leon Williams, to all the men I made answer some very personal questions, and to Mum and Dad for bearing with and being brilliant.

P.E-P

Characters

MARK, *sixteen, dopey-eyed*
JOHN, *twenty-seven, cruel jaw*

Note on Play

WINK *should be performed with movement and music.*

/ in the text indicates that the next person should come in on a slight overlap.

– in the text means that the speech should run continuously from person to person.

Cultural references can be updated to fit the time of the production as long as it fits the rhythm.

This text went to press before the end of rehearsals and so may differ slightly from the play as performed.

MARK. Today is a normal day. I've only been on Facebook five times, the Daily Mash twice and Reddit once. I have also played some COD, some GTA and some Wii Bowling but only because my little brother, Aaron, made me it's called 'quality time'… we do it whilst eating Coco Pops and I hope he doesn't ever grow up because then Mum will probably start buying adult stuff like muesli. Wank.

I look at porn for T-minus two minutes, just Amateur, Gagging and then one second of Gonzo, because I'm trying to time myself now and I'm getting better, more like an Olympic porn-watching athlete. I like to splice the scenes together till it's like a compilation mix, 'Now That's What I Call Really Good Porn '86'.

Then I catch my older sister trying to copy Nicki Minaj in 'Anaconda', which is embarrassing and a bit sick-making and then I get ready for school.

School is a bit crap but it's also alright. I feel like today might be good, that's what I think, then I think no, Mark, it will probably be a bit shit like every other day at school. So I decide to stare at the wall for a bit till my eyes hurt and then I think maybe I'll just hold my breath and die. I try this but I always end up taking a breath and anyway Aaron starts chucking things at my balls.

I check my phone, I have no texts, five Snapchats and no WhatsApps, two Facebook notifications – one to like Animal Farm so that doesn't count – and two new followers on Instagram which is pretty good.

I put my headphones on and walk to school, listening to shuffle and hoping no one can hear it when something a bit embarrassing comes on, like Jessie J.

I ignore all of the other people going to all the other schools, I listen to music and I feel safe, in a bubble, hand on my phone, texting, talking connected. A girl nearly gets run over, she tells the driver to 'fuck off'.

I see Mr Martin enter the school gates ahead of me, looking like a bit of shit today, ruffled tie, messy hair but he also totally thinks he's it, he is, you can see him being checked out by every single girl at the bus stop – he's what my mum would call 'a flirt'. I think he probably wasn't allowed to teach at the all-girls' school.

I go in.

JOHN. Monday morning and I've only been to bed for four hours – the amount of time you have to put in to having an affair – it's actually pretty intense. I have a fumble of my balls, before I spring out of bed and I think I might still be drunk because I'm not yet hungover. Check Facebook on my phone – just because, then BBC Sports, *Guardian* comments and a little bit of *Daily Mail* online because *Celeb Big Brother* is actually quite good at the moment. I make a coffee not just for me but for Claire also – see I can be an alright boyfriend sometimes, 'can't I, darling?' she takes one sip – spits in the sink – 'please don't buy Kenco, you dildo' and she's gone and already late for work, but I'm bang on time, baby, I always am. Get in the car and put the radio on loud. It's only a ten-minute drive but I'm fucked if I'm walking. Get out the car and buy a coffee from the kiosk outside the station – girl at the counter always gives me a smile – bless her she's got absolutely no tits but she's worth a good chirps for that extra squirt of espresso, 'see you tomorrow, darlin'' – nice touch. Check my phone again and get happn up – who have I 'crossed paths with' this morning? – nope not a fitty among 'em – and I swear she's at the girls' school 'twenty-one' – I wish. The Head comes up, phone away quickly, and says he's impressed by my latest GCSE results – 'I'm clearly an excellent addition to the faculty' – I give him my best – 'oh please it's hardly all down to me'. I love the way he takes my sycophancy seriously.

Now this is the bit where I slow down, pretend I'm looking out for all the boys coming in – 'tuck that shirt in, Oliver', 'don't run like a girl, Stefan, you're embarrassing yourself', et cetera. It's kinda fun. I like to wait till every last little runt has run in – means I don't have to come in early and prep my classroom – we have TAs to do that shit honestly.

I watch Mr Murphy rock up in his GT, shame my only mate at this school is a bit thicker than I would've liked. But he lends me a fag so I can hold off on the e-cigarette. I burp up a bit of sick as I sip on more black coffee but it's making my eyes itchy. Now I am so fucking hungover.

'How come – it's a Monday, mate?'

Sly smile he knows I've shagged Anna again.

'You better watch out that I don't tell Claire one day' but I know she would never believe him.

Daniel Wilson walks past with his hand down the back of an Alleyn's girl's school skirt – cosy. It makes me think of Claire – same flicked-back fringe that I didn't like at first – thought she was trying too hard to be trendy. And I miss Claire suddenly.

'Come on, dipshit, school bell innit.'

I have Year shitting Eleven first today and to be honest I might just be sick on one of their heads.

MARK. First period is French which is actually my favourite lesson because, well, it's taught by Mr Martin and he's got to be one of the best teachers in the school because he lets us watch loads of racy French films and doesn't even bother fast-forwarding over all the sex bits. Nice one. Mr Martin just has a way about it him you know – like this smile he does when he's sort of taking the piss out of you but he's also fully noticed you – I think it must be why girls can smell him a mile away – like he's some sort of animal man.

JOHN. Right Year Eleven, the wankers as I affectionately call them, a pitiful sight, all acne scars and crap stubble. God knows English teenagers are just the ugliest fuckbags in the world aren't they…

Right repeat after me: '*nous allons a la bibliotheque avec Dominique*', whoever Dominique is she sounds well fit.

Text message.

MARK. 'Sir, your phone, sir, you always say we're not allowed phones.'

JOHN. Shut the fuck up, you little –

'That's enough, Mark, I apologise, class, yup my bad didn't turn it off this morning.'

MARK. 'Sir, are you hanging?'

And yes I know most of the class are noticing my use of the slang, nice one.

JOHN. Not enough time spent in the shower clearly…

'Alright, lads, might have had a few beers last night but hey who can tell me what that is in French?'

See I am so down with the kids.

Mark puts his hand up this time, trying to win me back bless him, he's one of the thickest but he tries hard, on some sort of scholarship for sport, so he's clearly the povvo one, and God knows he's hardly winning in the looks department. Good luck to him.

'Yes, Mark?'

MARK. 'What's hangover in French?'

JOHN. 'Why on earth would you need to know that, Mark, had one have you?'

Ooh they love it when I take the piss and thank Christ the coffee's kicked in because now I'm on a roll, French verbs, infinitive, past participle and we're off as one by one I help root out the weak and promote the future Oxbridge tossers, and then the bell. Thank the Lord, one more cup of coffee and I might just make it through – don't you just love school.

MARK. At lunch I check my Facebook page.

JOHN. I have a coffee.

MARK. And Twitter.

JOHN. Followed by a cigarette.

MARK. And Instagram.

JOHN. Followed by a shitty hummus sandwich because the school's gone all Jamie Oliver and you can't get anything with a high salt content.

MARK. I also Snapchat a few people what looks like an ass crack but is just my elbows held together.

JOHN. Fucking apple crisps.

MARK. I talk to Rob and Ashleigh who have only been my mates since Year Nine when I got my scholarship and everyone realised it was for sports and not for something shit like choir or music. Ashleigh is such a gay name but he's okay. We talk about going paintballing knowing that we don't really like each other enough to go paintballing.

JOHN. I scroll through Tinder because I like the distraction – see that I have a couple of texts from Anna, 'last night was seriously crazy' apparently. I can't be bothered to reply – she is a great shag though, insecure women always are, eager and kinky. She follows it up with a picture of her in the bathroom mirror – I don't think grown women should send toilet selfies, leave that to the desperate sixteen-year-olds please. I can see her son's bath toys in the background – what my students would call an 'epic fail'. Mr Murphy has snuck in a bag of Wotsits, thank fuck, as we eat them like contraband we read out Anna's text messages – Mr Murphy does a really good psycho voice.

MARK. Ashleigh shows us a picture of what he says are 'Miss America via Chatroulette's tits', they are so blatantly not hers it's funny. Her message underneath is filthy and really puts me off my packet of soggy apple crisps. Sometimes it's like I can smell too much, I used to think that was my superpower and if it was, then that really fucking sucked.

On the stage bit where the teachers sit I see Mr Martin
looking lechy at his phone, probs looking at the same thing
we are.

JOHN. All of Anna's messages have got me feeling a little bit
excited, Mr Murphy goes to 'get a bit of exercise' which is
code for one last fag, and so I decide to text Claire
something explicit in my last few minutes of freedom. There
done it. She sends me a load of wink emoticons back. I think
she's taking the piss. It's been ages since she's been
interested in sex. Oh well looks like we're back to acting like
we couldn't care less.

MARK. Still looking over to where Mr Martin sits and I can't
help but think 'how the hell did he end up as a teacher?' Like
it's a bit depressing, to be fair he could've been a male
model or a stripper, something with a bit more money in it.
He looks like he's smudged at the edges today, but he's still
sharp in his nose and mouth. I wish I was better at French.

JOHN. Before that final bell rings hard into my tequila-swollen
brain I stare out into a sea of students licking the cheap food
out of their hideous retainers, laughing at each other's crap
banter and trying so hard to keep hidden boners as the cheap
uniforms stretch over their fat arses. Jesus the stench of
Lynx and hormones is enough to make me want to light a
match and see the polyester go up in flames. Thank God I'm
in my twenties.

MARK. Ashleigh's top at French because his parents have a
timeshare in Brittany.

Everything Ashleigh has is better than what I have, new
iPhone, proper Nikes, two Apple Macs for no reason, and an
iPad Air because his dad is a pushover and gives him
everything he wants. He's even fingered Michelle Hogan
after the Year Nine joint school play when everyone went
round to Stefan's house and I stood guard outside the
downstairs toilet, because all these dicks have a downstairs
toilet for shitting in. Final bell rings and I make out I've
gotta go for a piss so that I can have some 'me time'.

JOHN. Final bell and I make my way to Year Eight – who are actually still quite sweet but not in a thick way like Year Seven –

Mark bumps into me dozy git, God he really is well a bit wet, and I want to tell him now that if he doesn't try harder he is going to be eaten alive, that he will be one of those guys that no one invites on the pub crawl and no one in their right mind wants to share a communal kitchen with in halls.

I miss uni then – miss meeting Claire for the very first time, fucking everything in sight and making lots of very pretty girls cry. He won't survive ten seconds in the real world.

'Get to class, Mark. Now.'

MARK. 'Just going toilet that alright, sir?' and I even mutter 'Jesus' which is sort of pushing it.

In the loos I look at porn for T-minus fifty-five seconds, which is super-fast, and I think I'm getting better and handling my addiction, which is actually really grown up. I have a sister who is a bit anorexic so I think my family is really good at will power. I mean Mum hasn't had a drink since Dad died, and she says that's why no one invites her anywhere.

JOHN. Now for the long slog of the afternoon, everyone farting down the corridors wishing it to be four o'clock it will come, it always comes, then it's home, eat, marking, TV, bed, miserable, but hey at least we can go to the pub – what can these poor fuckers do to pass the time – I mean they don't even have happy slapping nowadays what do they do?

MARK. Apparently after school a load of people are going to the park to meet a bunch of Alleyn's girls and everyone is trying to get invited, or if not, everyone now intends to go to the park after school. I don't, I go home following my sister Shannon, ignoring each other till she turns left before our house so she can have a 'secret smoke'.

JOHN. Home time at last and I've already technically overdosed on Nurofen. I get in my car and play a lot of very loud and aggressive music that to quote Claire 'demeans women', the hangover has lifted and I'm thinking that I might get closer to Claire tonight – maybe we'll watch a film, something she chooses and I will pretend to like, and have a laugh for once.

See Mark Taylor wobbling after some stick-thin schoolgirl from the state school round the corner – fuck me has he actually got a girlfriend. Nice one.

MARK. I get home and play Fifa, COD, and let Aaron hit me in the head with the sofa cushions till Mum comes home from work. We eat pizza, Shannon won't have the cheese or the crusts, Mum sighs. I go upstairs and log on, I log on for seven hours.

And it's like my whole room opens up, space, time and all the continuums. My desk is just a small spaceship that floats around, spinning, orbiting this – I dunno massive gateway of stuff – all the stuff in the world and it is amazing, because I can get Google to speak to me in French and I can play cock or balls on Skype with Rob till 3 a.m., play World of Warcraft with some dicks from Salisbury, watch a load of porn in a range of languages and get asked out by three paedos in Malta. Websites explode like stars on my screen with adverts and add-ons and poker sites and YouTube videos. I sign up for web forums, DJ sites, I enter competitions to win Virgin Mobile goodies, tickets to V Festival and a chance to meet Taylor Swift. I watch a documentary on extra-terrestrial beings and learn what an infected cock ring looks like. I am wired, awake, my mind full, my eyes fuller. I can't even blink any more but I can't stop looking, staring into this space where everyone else is.

JOHN. I'm home and Claire is waiting for me, she looks a bit hacked off at me already as if she knows I've been singing the n-word loudly in my car – what? It's in the lyrics…

'You like my text earlier?'

'Yeah really made me laugh' she smirks and then puts a pan of pasta on.

Delicious –

'Did you pick up any pesto?'

'No.'

Back out I go.

I pick up pesto and two bottles of Pinot Grigio – one each –

I pour her a glass of wine and tell her how much I thought about her today, she grimaces, for the first time ever it dawns on me that maybe she's having an affair, that we are both having affairs. We might even have chlamydia.

MARK. I look at my Facebook profile, because I like to keep on top of how other people see me and Ashleigh has just uploaded all the photos from the school trip to Ypres, some of which are really embarrassing and he keeps fucking tagging me in them. There are pictures of us with Mr Martin looking at battlefields and everyone getting bored and Fred Rowson throwing up at the back of the coach which we got stuck on for seven hours and Mr Martin being a hero and buying us all a can of Coke afters and not minding when Michael David bought a bottle of whiskey, because he already has a full-on moustache and is six foot fucking five, and let us all add a bit. Because Mr Martin is the only teacher who people fight to sit next to at the front of the coach to try and impress with our knowledge of obscure jokes from *Peep Show*. The next photos on my profile are of me at Thorpe Park with Aaron and Mum, Shannon looking fucked off in the background, no one having a good time. Then we're back to photos of the summer before Dad died, me running in the nationals, Dad holding a banner with my name on, all of us at Sennen eating hot dogs by the sea. But most recent are just pictures of me in school-uniform poses, putting flab where muscle was, looking like you could make cheese from my fucking forehead. As far away from Mr Martin as you could possibly get.

Then I google him because for some reason he's never not a bit in my brain, he's sort of what I think I would like to be, maybe, Mr Martin, and he's there: Facebook, Twitter account,

I stalk him on Facebook, privacy settings the wanker, in a relationship with Claire Stokes, click on Claire Stokes, idiot – no privacy settings – clearly a bit of a dipshit. Jeeezus twenty-five photo albums. I look through all of them.

JOHN. Claire has a shower whilst I watch the pan simmer – I open up my laptop, mark some papers, look at *Guardian Jobs*, think about moving to France, living where I did on my year abroad and not giving a fuck. I start to watch porn with the mute button on – danger-wanking like a fucking fifteen-year-old, but hey anything to pass the time right – perhaps if Claire watched porn she would be more enthusiastic in bed. Maybe she'd even wax. I get Facebook up and get ready to take the piss out of whichever twat from school is getting married next but Claire's comes up instead of mine.

MARK. They live in a really small flat in Crystal Palace, she has a best mate called Emily – who looks like a bit of a bitch, a mum and dad who wear padded waistcoats and have a stupidly large dog and a stupidly small one, works at Lloyds Bank, went to Edinburgh Uni, likes the colour red, speaks Spanish, did an MA in Business Management, likes listening to alt-J, is in Stitch and Bitch Gypsy Hill, watches the rugby and sometimes the tennis, has been a bridesmaid five times, fancies Ryan Reynolds like mega, might be going to the Blues Kitchen Shoreditch, can't get enough of *Serial*, simply hates froyo, once got a dip-dye which got fifty-three likes.

She is beautiful.

JOHN. I leave Claire's profile up and think about fraping her but I'm not that sad, look through her pictures, thank God she got rid of the dip-dye. Then I flick through photos of me, of us, of me, of us, of me, of us, of me, of us, of me – and it looks like we are one pretty great couple – but then the photos stop and that was a while ago – was that when I started seeing Anna and she started seeing someone else? When was the last time we did anything that made us look like that?

MARK. I can't stop clicking through their life – it's kinda fascinating, like a really big game of Guess Who? – and she feels so real to me, keep seeing her face smile at me from the screen, her holding the keys to their flat, her making him wear a naked-man apron, them holding hands on a beach and I think that's me there on that beach holding her hand – that's where I want to be.

JOHN. It's odd looking at us this way through a timeline of events that make up – Jesus seven years of just this? Flick to my Facebook for a second just to see what my profile says about me – not much other than my obsession with Uni Lad and Netflix TV. At least Claire's makes me look interesting.

MARK. But it's not me on that beach, it's Mr Martin, the kind of man who gets with women like Claire, has a proper life and a house and everything you could ever want. So I create a profile, a new one.

I am Tim Walker, I am twenty-eight and I work at Lloyds Bank. I am interested in funny pictures of cats, tae kwon do and *The Inbetweeners* (show her I have a GSOH). I stroll through Google Images creating myself a life, holidays, cars, picnics, beaches, tennis matches, pubs, bars, restaurants, Instagrams of posh lunches, people smiling, selfies in the mirror, pecs, muscles, taut, toned, good underwear, better shirts, but not too posh an element of East London hipster – I include 'my love of art like Banksy'. I am 'hashtag blessed' and 'hashtag luvin life', and 'hashtag living for the weekend' because that's just the kind of thing I want to be. I don't know why I do any of this, except for maybe because I can. Then I tell Shannon she's a fat slag on Twitter and look up laws on pretending to be someone else on Facebook.

Then I add Claire and wait for her to confirm request.

JOHN. Friend request comes up – Tim Walker, looks like a knob, works where Claire works, eats a lot of posh food. He has no other mates, dodgy, but his profile is new, created today, bit late on this, mate. Status update:

MARK. 'lol deleted my Facebook like a right tosser having to start again –

JOHN. – good chance to get rid of some right losers.' I click accept by accident, oh well so what, but I'm jealous, in fact I'm really fucking jealous, what if the guy she's sleeping with is Tim? Timothy Walker, the knob who holidays in Ibiza. I hate Tim. I text Anna.

MARK. Friend request accepted, what do I do next?

JOHN. We spend the rest of the evening in front of the telly, I stroke behind her ear till she tells me to stop it. An advert for Lloyds comes up which makes her sigh, she says that she hates her job *again*.

'What about the people who work there?'

'Oh they're alright actually, I suppose that's one thing to stick around for.'

For the people, the men, like Tim. Fucking hell she's definitely shagging Tim. I get a text from Anna, 'not tonight, that we should stop this, that I'm driving her mad' fucking drama queen, it's only sex, why does everyone these days seem to be getting so upset about sex?

MARK. Should I message her? What should I say? I decide to play Minecraft till 3 a.m. instead – don't want to come across too keen – Shannon always says that puts her right off.

JOHN. It's three in the morning and I can't sleep, get my laptop up and see Claire lying next to me illuminated by the screen, she doesn't look real, surely she's not actually cheating on me. I stagger into the kitchen in my pants and message Tim.

MARK. That noise, an actual message from Claire, from a real person, from a real live woman. Fuck. She says: 'hi how are you Tim? Do you wish you were with me right now?' Shit, man, Mr Martin's girl is a right player. Wink emoticon. She means business.

'Of course I do babes, yur well fit.'

JOHN. Confirmation, an affair, fuck you, Claire.

'My boyfriend checks my Facebook', too right he does, so let's take this to what um email? I'm guessing he already has her number the fucker. It takes me two minutes to come up with a new address: stokes101@hotmail.com.

MARK. 'Right yeah gotta be careful, in which case babe you should totally take my email.' I get Yahoo up quick, it's gotta be something that Tim would have, but not a funny one, that's just obvious teenager, um, Timthetank@yahoo.com really no one already has that? Just press send.

JOHN. I delete all signs of having just added Tim 'the supposed Tank' on Claire's Facebook and get back in bed. Then I can't help but have another look at Claire's photos – see if I can spot Tim lurking in the background, I scroll through till I find the first photo and it's of Claire at uni looking quiet and resilient and for a second I touch the screen.

MARK. I finally go to sleep, taking her email address to bed with me, and have dreams of running down corridors, spinning Chatroulette and lots of eyes winking at me, at one point I see my face repeated in every screen in every house and then it's Mr Martin's face on top of mine and we're sort of blinking together over and over and it makes me feel a bit mental and well tired when I wake up, but then I repeat to myself, stokes101@hotmail.com and I feel for the first time since winning the county final a power in myself. I email her, 'morning beautiful' with a picture of a sunrise – too much? Shit perhaps too much.

JOHN. Fucking hell this Tim Walker's a bit of a stalker, cheesy git has already sent me a sunrise this morning and a promise of breakfast in bed. I make Claire a cup of tea in protest. She says she hasn't got time and runs out of the house looking smart and perhaps a little guilty. I text Anna that 'I want to fuck her hard up against a wall'. No response. I leave both cups of tea cold on the draining board and leave for school.

MARK. I nearly miss registration I'm all glazed over with this feeling of, what is it, like a tingling, it's not quite the

beginnings of a boner, it's more like pins and needles all over
– even Rob is saying I look like I've let a really sly one rip. I
have something all to myself but I'm not letting go of it.

JOHN. I didn't realise how much Claire wasn't that in to me, it's
been seven years for fucksake I thought it was only me who
needed distracting – so where does this leave me – does she
know about Anna – is she just doing this to get back at me? I
mean fucking hell why are we still together then? – Because
the people we're shagging don't have what we really need –
an expensive flat and crap nights in front of the TV?

Still no response from Anna I chain-smoke all the way to the
school gates where I connect the new email account to my
phone – see if Tim Walker has sent me anything else
sickeningly romantic. I want to meet the tosser and leave
him brain-damaged.

I tell him with a smirk that 'I want to make love to him under
that sunrise', it makes me feel weird pretending to be Claire
like this, I feel exposed, I feel like I'm back on the wrong
side of school.

MARK. Oh man, she's going to want to have actual sex with
Tim, one day, maybe, under a sunrise apparently. I feel sick,
I feel clammy, I feel like Shannon does when she's having a
'period'. What do I do now? I think about telling Rob and
Ashleigh but I know they would fuck it up, tell Mr Martin
what a weirdo I'm being. I don't want this to be over already.
How long does it take to get a six-pack? I look up steroids on
the internet and send her some memes of cats to keep her
interested instead.

JOHN. Jesus Christ Tim's a bit of a twat just keeps sending me
memes of cats, what the fuck is that about, does Claire
actually like this crap? Right French class again what a
surprise Year Eleven… I can't even remember if I gave them
homework or not… and do I really give a fuck.

MARK. I feel a bit weird looking at Mr Martin in French,
knowing what I know, makes me sit up a bit, meet his eye – is
that a bit odd? I wish I could show someone Claire's
messages, show them that someone is finally interested in me.

JOHN. 'Right turn to the test on page twenty-one and yes I know you've all figured out that the answers are in the back of the book but if anyone looks I will call him a poof for the rest of term. Understood?'

MARK. I look at my phone under my desk, stop sending her memes, Mark, she clearly doesn't like it, she hasn't replied to the last three and I thought they were all pretty funny. I need help clearly, think like Tim, think like Mr Martin – what does he say to Claire that makes her like him – but then why would she want to talk to Tim when she already has someone like him. Maybe his banter isn't as good as he thinks it is…

JOHN. 'Mark, hand your phone over now.'

MARK. 'No I, sorry, sir, please I'll put it in my bag, sir.'

JOHN. 'It's sitting on my desk till the bell for lunch no arguments.'

God you'd think I'd just asked him to get out his dick.

'Now, Mark.'

MARK. 'Yes, sir.'

Fucking hell what if the screen isn't locked and what if /

JOHN. / 'Who's that old man on your background?'

MARK. 'My dad, sir' and the room goes extra-silent kinda quiet.

JOHN. 'Fine take it back – it's lunchtime in a minute anyway.'

MARK. 'Thanks, sir.'

Pause.

At lunch I tell Rob and Ashleigh that I've got extra homework – that I need to go to the school library – but actually I just need an excuse not to look at my phone for a bit. Why am I such a prick? I log on to the school computers and stare at the screen where a reply from Claire should be.

JOHN. Surprised to see the dipshit that is Mark Taylor in the actual library, still feel a bit weird about what's just happened actually – I suppose a bit of me understands how he feels, but I'm not exactly going to start a 'dead dad's society'. I focus on photocopying exercise books fuck me my life is shit. Stare at my phone for a bit, background of Claire at the beach looking pretty fit in a white bikini – the last time we liked each other enough to book a joint holiday. Look back at Tim's messages, come on, mate, surely you wanna spice things up with more than just pictures of cats in big hats. I look through my photo library, sure I must have something of Claire in here, or are those Anna's nope hers are more lopsided.

Send Tim one of Claire to get him excited.

MARK. These aren't like Miss America via Chatroulette's tits these are real tits, can I send a dick pic at school? Google dicks, nope barred on the school internet. If I rubbed it really hard and zoomed in I could make it look a bit bigger than it is?

JOHN. Fuck me is Mark Taylor banging one off by the school computers, surely even he wouldn't do something as socially retarded as that… Look back at more pictures of Claire's tits, maybe I do prefer them to Anna's after all.

I send him some more 'these babes are gunna be all yours'.

MARK. Wow I think Claire must really like me that's a lot of tit pics she just sent me, this is probably the best day of my life actually ever, even better than the day I ran all the way to Waterloo Bridge with Dad and he bought me my first proper pint and we sat surrounded by people and couples on the South Bank and it felt fucking wicked, like I was a person in time and space with everyone else, just moving with everyone and everything. Then I see Mr Martin looking at me, it looks like he knows, fuck does he know? He can't know what his girlfriend just sent me – ha if he asked for my phone now – I put Claire's tits as my new screensaver that will impress him next time. I give him a smile.

JOHN. I think Mark Taylor just smirked at me – wanker – sometimes I wish I could hit them, walk around with a really long ruler just smacking the sides of their spot-covered faces.

I snap out of it just as the bell rings – get through the rest of the afternoon and then it's the end of another dull day. I run to the loos as the kids all exit, nothing more awkward than when the head teacher needs a slash at the same time so I use the disabled loos on the first floor – so sue me. Look into the mirror then down at what I'm carrying – Tim better be packing. I tell Tim to send me something – want to see just what exactly is my competition. Can't remember the last time I even felt intimidated by somebody, especially in this department. Then I take my very first toilet selfie and I send it to Anna – wait for the inevitable, she better respond quickly. Bet she'll beg me to stick it in her. Hey at least Anna will always want me.

MARK. I just can't do it, can't send one, feels wrong, maybe a bit, I dunno, dirty somehow – like in her profile she's this whole person and all I have so far are bits of her that don't add up. I want to see her smile because she's seen me in a crowd. But maybe this is how it all starts?

Pasta for dinner and Shannon isn't even trying to eat it; Aaron is licking the rim of his cup like a special so I kick him under the table. Sometimes I hate him, being so small still, it's like he doesn't even remember Dad at all sometimes, just cries because Mum does. The table is quiet, it's like we're all just swallowing too loud. Mum says 'maybe we should all watch a film tonight' and no one answers. In my room safe and sound I put music on full volume and just sit there, drowning everything out till my ears buzz and there's nothing left to think about. I flick through some porn to see if I can take a screen grab and send it to Claire – if it's too big it might not be believable but isn't that what women want?

But I just can't seem to find the right one.

JOHN. I sit in the car for a bit, just, well, because it delays the inevitable marking – and I listen to something really, really emo for my liking, it's a song all about killing the guy's girlfriend and it's oddly satisfying. I wonder how much longer I will have Claire for, and how the hell do we start to sort out who gets what with the flat? Maybe that's why we haven't left each other, because it's actually quite a lot of effort.

When I finally get in she's left me a note – 'gone out for dinner with the girls – expect me drunk – don't worry I'll get an Uber'. Yeah right she's gone to meet him, I can smell her perfume everywhere and she's worn it for the 'Tank'. I crack on to that other bottle of Pinot Grigio and start marking in my pyjamas. There are sites where you can Photoshop the head of someone you don't like onto a dummy and then kick them off a tall building repeatedly – I take a picture of Tim off Facebook and look at it till my eyes get tired. I can't be bothered. Watch some hard-core porn instead – get tired of seeing the mascara run down some poor bitch's cum-stained face, so I turn to Lad Bible and watch shitty videos of dogs welcoming war heroes instead. Then play my favourite game of leaving abusive comments under feminist *Guardian* articles, what can I say I like to see them wind themselves up in petty arguments, 'yeah, yeah argue harder bitch'. Then before I know it, it's 10 p.m. and I'm ready for bed and I get in the covers and wait for Claire to come home.

MARK. I decide I'm going to do some research to impress Claire, so I raid Shannon's DVD collection and watch *He's Just Not That Into You*, *27 Dresses*, *PS I Love You*, *Just Like Heaven* and a *Walk to Remember*. It starts to blur into one big wedding cake and I'm pretty sure all women want is to be kissed in the rain and the promise of eternal love. What's disappointing is that there's no proper sex in any of them – not one – I suppose girls just like to stop at the kissing bit unless they're porn stars – but then those women are just different. I check my phone, her tits are still staring at me, I haven't said anything back yet, it's not that I'm scared to, just don't know yet what Tim would do.

JOHN. Claire gets into bed stinking of Chardonnay and Prezzo and tells me all about how Lauren is breaking up with Sean and I think – 'are any of these people even my mates? – and 'hold on don't use this lame story to cover up your date'. 'Lauren and Sean were about to get married' she sighs –

'what a waste of time eh – what a waste of two lives'. We stare at the ceiling in silence and she holds my hand under the duvet, I'm about to say I love you, but she takes it away.

MARK. I dream about Mr Martin holding my hand down the school corridors, helping me get to the bathroom and when he opens the door there's mirrors everywhere and us staring back at ourselves but it's like I'm watching from above too – then the lights flicker and suddenly Mr Martin is lying on the floor and he starts to dissolve like a horror movie, like *House of Wax* or some shit like that. I stand there just laughing. Jesus I need to sort my dreams out. I get ready for school – but first I send Claire a message 'I wish I was waking up with you'.

JOHN. I fucking wish I was too, Tim, but this morning Claire has already got up and gone for a hangover-guilt run. I stretch out and think of living alone again, and realise I haven't actually done such a thing. 'What's the point?' I think and yet I still get up and go to work, just put my clothes on and walk out the front door.

MARK. Mr Martin walks just a bit ahead of me, back hunched clutching a coffee. I feel like we're connected, like a wire could be drawn from him to me, a lifeline, a puppet string or something. I try to get in time with his footsteps and copy his walk. I do it so no one notices like I'm a really good shadow and with every footstep I try and get a little bit closer.

JOHN. At lunch I can still feel my hand pulsing where Claire held it and I feel oddly numb. Mr Murphy sits next to me and starts going on about how he and Ms King from Chemistry definitely had a moment at the pub last night and he can't wait to brag at me for once, what does he want a fucking pat on the back? I look at my phone for something else, I dunno, a sign or something that tells me why I'm here. But there are no answers, no messages, no Facebook notifications, no emails, not even fucking Anna is responding. Mr Murphy gets up and leaves me at the table with nothing but my packaged sandwich and I feel stand-alone, surrounded by teenagers with hope in their eyes and still time to have and do everything. I want to scream at them, I want to tell them not to worry because their lives will be shit too and everything you think you want will never, ever come to you, that it's harder than that, than this, that maybe, maybe you will have a few hours here and there of bliss, sit on a mountain and take some photos for another Facebook album, meet someone, fall for someone, think that you two are the best thing ever only to end up bored hating the sight of one another's orgasm face. I text Claire that 'I miss her today' – but I send it as a message to Tim instead.

MARK. I ignore Rob and Ashleigh's plan to sit in the PE block after school and smoke the shit bits of spliff his brother will give him, I have to think about Claire instead – she says she misses me – 'I miss her too' I say, and I mean it, she's the only real thing I've got. I can feel myself getting older I think, I stroke my chin – yup there are definitely some hairs that weren't there the other morning.

JOHN. I tell Mr Murphy we're going to the pub, I don't tell him anything about Claire or Anna or Tim, I just buy round after round of pints – a shot of vodka in each and I let Mr Murphy's words spew over me, the sexist jokes and the homophobic banter and I let his hate fuel me – because I want to be angry.

I decide I'm going to have sex with Claire tonight. I email Tim telling him how horny I am, taking the piss out of Claire who can't even say the word cunt. I use some of Anna's best lines till it sounds like a script from a budget porno, it's all fuck me with this, cocks and dildos.

MARK. Jeezus man this is getting raunchy. I think she must want me to reply but I don't know what to say, it's like it's always easier in your head but out loud it's just well embarrassing. So I tell her: 'hey, hi, hun' delete um 'babe, that snds well gd, I want to do tings to you too, like um yeah hot stuff'.

'What your man can't do for you, winky face, smiley, kiss, two kisses' delete 'one kiss'.

JOHN. 'Right yeah what my man can't do, loads of things actually, he's a bit shit at life in general, can't make a woman happy that's for sure, well he can make other women happy but not me. Sad face.'

MARK. 'Yeah I know he's a right dick' delete, delete 'he looks on fb like a right dick, he treat you bad? Angry emoticon.'

'I make up for it.'

'Babe'… delete. 'Kiss', no wait she didn't put any… no kiss.

JOHN. 'Nah he just a bit, a bit' delete, 'he's a bit shit, he doesn't tell me how lucky he is ever, he doesn't make me feel special, he doesn't tell me how beautiful I am, he doesn't make an effort, we don't have sex, he comes back smelling of other women, dickhead'. There's no emoticon for that, 'kiss' instead.

MARK. Right so Mr Martin is why Claire needs Tim, because he's a dick and she needs rescuing. It makes sense really he goes around school with that permanent smirk, making everyone feel that fucking small and I realise that he's just not very nice. So wait Mr Martin isn't the guy I want to be – it's Tim, Tim's the man for me, for Claire. I can be what she needs.

So I tell her: 'I want to see her, hold her face in my hands and kiss her hard on the lips'. Like they do in that film Shannon always watches and cries over, *The Notebook*, it's the best one trust me. And I send her lots of kisses.

And I know, I know this isn't a movie and I'm not some built guy like Tim who can walk in and fuck Mr Martin up and like I dunno kill him and take her and pick her up like in a Lynx advert and carry her off. But I sort of think that if I could I would. Yeah I would. I won't let her down like he did.

I won't leave her like Dad did.

I feel for the first time in ages like going for a really, really long run and running so hard my mouth tastes like acid.

JOHN. Tim's last message makes me kick a lamp post well dream on, you fuckwit, because I'm the one that's going to kiss her and shag her, I'm the one she really wants.

MARK. I get my trainers on and it's been a while, and before I leave the house I think about what it was like when Dad was there at the finish line, waiting, cheering, smiling for the whole time. I don't even warm up, I just hit it at full speed.

JOHN. I get home, drop my keys, loosen tie, jacket on the floor, Claire is already in her pyjamas looking pissed off at the TV, she can hear I'm drunk and her shoulders are hunched. She's trying so hard not to tell me off. I hate how she knows that I know that she knows and we can't even be bothered to say it to each other. I think what if Tim's been here in my front room; at least I've never had Anna round, not once, I'm not that much of a prick. I pull her hair from behind the sofa and she looks confused. I think she thinks I'm playing; I don't know what I want, I sort of want to hurt her. I kiss her upside down and it's messy. And I know I must smell of beer and cigarettes but it's a taste that reminds her of uni and she kisses me back.

MARK. I hear every slap of my foot against the pavement. I rush past people, squeeze round lamp posts, jump over cracks and hit the park at full tilt. I run and run harder, heart –

JOHN. – beating faster and faster. I can hear hers thumping against mine as we push into the staircase and she fumbles with my belt as I fumble with the buttons on her pyjama top – she takes it off for me and her nipples look at me and I kiss them and she moans and bites my neck and that means it's on –

MARK. – to the top of the park where you can see the whole of Herne Hill just spread and you're high up near the sun coming down, and for seconds you're blinded but you don't mind because in a way the whiteness makes you feel like your mind has disappeared –

JOHN. – and as she sits on top of me my back hits against the stairs again and again till I know it must be bruising, internally bleeding, but the pain just adds to the intensity as she grabs my neck and we twist round till it's her turn to feel the burn of the carpet and –

MARK. – faster and faster my feet pounding the grass, the gravel, the tarmac of the playground, my chest burning, my ribcage contracting till it feels like the bones are piercing my insides –

JOHN. – and I grab at her throat until she can't breathe and I jam myself inside her harder and harder as her face gets redder and I only stop when her hand grabs my arm so tight and she digs her nails in and it's such a thin light line between pain and pleasure. I release her neck and the red fades from her face to her chest where I collapse in shuddered breaths.

MARK. When I get home my mum is watching telly, she looks like a crumpled heap of clothes that are slightly dirty, like one of those beach balls with all the air taken out. She looks like someone who isn't really my mum. I used to wipe my face on her face and that makes me feel odd. I should go and sit down next to her, ask her about the storyline – pretend like I give a shit about *Corrie* and *EastEnders*, tell her I went for a run and it felt odd not to have Dad egging me on. But I just stand in the doorway and then I leave. She has Aaron if she really wanted company.

JOHN. Claire and I don't talk like we used to after sex, we don't stay up all night trying to engage in second and third rounds, we don't tug and compare like kids do at nursery school, we just go to bed, and I feel like I got what I wanted and nothing at all. I think I might cry but I haven't done that in a really long time. I clench my half of the duvet and think 'fuck this I'm totally losing it'. I check my phone because for some reason I just need to know that he's there on the other end.

I stare at his profile for the thirteenth time today, just scroll and scroll for no reason but to see the man that Claire would rather be with, or does she still love me? I don't know what to think, I need to see who this guy is. So I do it.

'Friday night come round?'

MARK. I tell Shannon she's looking fat but she just tells me to go fuck myself, for once I don't do exactly that because I'm spent. I look at my emails instead, looking for Claire and see

a message that settles it once and for all – that Claire wants
to be with me just as much as I want to be with her. In fact
she wants me round hers this Friday night. I wish there was
someone here to high-five.

JOHN. Friday night I'm stuck in a gym hall telling thick rich
people that their children will be even thicker and not much
richer, but Claire is… Claire is… I have no effing clue, what
do we do on Friday nights? Go for a few with our
colleagues, see each other at home in bed, watch a film,
switch off, turn off, nothing mostly. Sometimes I see Anna
and shag her hard and fast before she starts moaning about
her rather shit life, that or play Fifa at Mr Murphy's sad
bachelor pad. But this Friday night is parent-teacher evening
and that's why it's perfect.

I tell Tim my address 'Flat 24B Colby Road', I'd have
thought he would've known that by now but maybe I was
wrong, maybe when I'm round at Anna's she's round at his.
Why are we bothering to pay rent?

MARK. Friday night I'm going round, because I think it's time
I grew up, in fact I think it's time I became a man, and I
know she's going to be shocked yeah, but maybe if I dress
smart and anyway she's clearly up for it right – and I'm not
Tim, but I am if you know what I mean. They're my words,
it's my head – how much more real can you get?

I will go to Mr Martin's house on parent-teacher evening, I
will go there and meet Claire, tell her that I am here for her
and she might laugh but she also might just let me in.

JOHN. In the morning I tell Claire that I finally changed the
internet provider, that they are coming round on Friday night
– 'that it's possible for her to be in right?'

She almost looks impressed with me – 'where will you be?'

'Parent-teacher evening I swear you never listen to me' – but
I say it with a smile and she gives me one back, it's been a
while, but maybe that's because she's already inviting 'Tim
the fucking Tank' round in her head, see flashes of them

fucking on our bed. We attempt a goodbye kiss before she leaves, but she says my breath stinks of coffee and she goes for my cheek.

MARK. Music in my ears I'm walking to school and when I see Mr Martin this time I feel, ha, I feel amazing. I think about that thing you used to say as a kid, 'I know something you don't know' and it feels fan-fucking-tastic. I suppose I should feel guilty, maybe, but I don't. I feel like I'm the one in control – look around me and see tons of teenagers all looking at their phones or feet and feeling trapped like specks of shit just following some crap routine but not me – I feel like shouting, jumping on cars and telling the world that I mean something to someone else. I feel like Rocky does in that bit – and yes all the music is pounding in my ears and I am finally excited about something.

JOHN. Driving in to school as usual and I glare at the turds that share the same pavement as me, the bossy-arsed mums with spoilt-as-fuck kids, see the dads in the Land Rovers and think about taking a massive shit on their windscreen. Fantasise about running every little prick on every single zebra crossing over, like this is just one big game of GTA and in a minute I can start cutting people's heads off and fucking a prostitute. Then I can't stop playing footage of Friday night round in my head, of Claire opening the door to Tim, being pleased to see him. I start to hit the side of my head repeatedly as if it's an image I can knock out of me.

I enter the school gates and Mr Murphy tells me 'I look like shit and do I have a migraine because I'm acting like I'm on something'.

'Stress, mate, stress about Friday.'

'It's only bloody parent-teacher evening, we'll get pissed after,' he reassures me.

'Sure thing' I say, just one more day, just keep grinning.

MARK. I can barely sit still in French, my skeleton just wants to leap out of my skin and break-dance all over the place. I can't stop sort of weirdly grinning at Mr Martin, feeling like he's the idiot to be patronised, that maybe he's just a guy, a loser that teaches French to a bunch of teenagers who don't even care, embarrassing or what?

Touch my phone in my pocket and know that it's like a sword or something from a film with magical powers – I am a sex-text demi-god here to rescue all teachers' girlfriends from their shitty boyfriends.

JOHN. Mark Taylor is gurning at me like a ferret and I'm trying so hard not to throw a bloody board-marker at his gigantic forehead. The Freak. To be honest I can barely teach today, can't stop thinking about what it's actually like between Claire and Tim, is their sex better, does she say yes to anal for him?

MARK. 'Sir, sir?'

JOHN. '*What*, Mark?'

MARK. 'You've not pressed play on the tape, sir.'

JOHN. 'Thank you, Mark, yeah sorry, class, too busy thinking of parent-teacher evenings and what lovely things I'm going to say about you guys, not. Now shut up and concentrate.'

Same goes for you, mate.

MARK. Shannon finds her DVDs in my room and knows something's up – says I better not be spunking off over chick flicks because then I'm really tweaked. I tell her she's an ugly prick and she knees me in the balls, it's the most we've talked in a while. I wish I could ask her what to say to Claire, ask her what I'm supposed to do – and whether she misses Dad too. After another silent dinner – spaghetti hoops – Jesus Mum isn't even trying any more. I go to bed, but I just can't sleep – tomorrow is the day and I am miles away from Tim – simple fact is I haven't a clue, so I watch a ton of RedTube, start with Amateur as that's probably what it will be most like, don't want to get my expectations too high – they warn you about that all the time. Aaron tries to come in – 'what you watching?' 'Research' I say and shut him out.

JOHN. Claire isn't in when I get home, a text, 'dinner with
    Mum'. Right, Tim again, her mum only ever comes to
    London when the Boxing Day sales are on – Jesus, Claire,
    can you at least try a little bit harder to keep it secret. I check
    her Instagram and there's a picture of her and her mum at
    Bill's, and it's raining outside like it is now – fair enough –
    suppose she knows she's seeing him tomorrow anyway. For
    a second I forget who I am in this game – Claire or Tim. I
    put a meal in the microwave and watch it rotate – think about
    when we first moved in and shagged on the kitchen floor –
    think we thought we were supposed to do all these things.

    I message Tim – 'one more sleep wink wink'. It feels like
    Christmas.

MARK. Mum is nervous about parent-teacher evening,
    changing her earrings and making throat-clearing noises like
    a really paranoid guinea pig. I've told her not to worry, I'm
    not exactly a trouble-maker, just a bit okay really. Not good,
    not bad, sort of average and that I haven't won any heats in
    running for ages, so not even the PE department can get
    excited. She looks at me when I mention running like her
    heart might crack and she's going to start blubbering so I
    change track. 'It'll be fine, Mum.'

    'Just got no one to go with, son.'

    Shannon slams a door shut and starts flushing and we all
    know what that means. Mum sags that little bit more, so I
    give her a hand-squeeze and show her out the door, 'make
    sure they eat something for tea' she pleads and I know she
    means Shannon more than she means Aaron.

    But I ain't got time to fry fish fingers, no fucking way, my
    mission is on, the clock is ticking and my cock is tingling. I
    am shit-scared. I grab at some Lynx, I clean in and around
    my pubes and get loads of annoying tissue-papery bits stuck
    to my, well, bits. Piss off Shannon by hogging the hot water,
    then dash into my best sports jumper, no wait – shirt – I've
    only got the one from the funeral but it will have to do. I spit
    a bit on my shoes… then swap 'em for trainers, much cooler
    – yeah if only I was a foot fucking taller.

JOHN. Enter the school hall and the parents all stare at me hopefully, like I'm a god, the power that decides if the money they've spent caring has been worth it, trust me it hasn't been – your kids are all dicks.

MARK. I get the number 3 bus to Crystal Palace, it takes twenty-five minutes according to Google Maps.

JOHN. 'Hello, Mrs Taylor, Mark's mother, yes I have him for French.'

MARK. I spend the whole twenty-five minutes thinking about everything they never teach you in sex-ed and everything you learn for yourself on the internet. Jesus how did people ever know how to have sex before the internet?

JOHN. No wonder Mark is such a div his mum is upsetting just to look at and most of these Dulwich mums are sort of milfy, she's just sort of beige – a sack of flesh and well, grief, it says on his notes in his record – Dad's dead go easy on them – we get it – Jeezus it doesn't excuse the BO does it…

MARK. I don't have any condoms does that matter? I just didn't know what size to buy –

I mean do you start low or aim high?

JOHN. I can't concentrate on the bullshit statement I've written about Mark's non-existent potential for French verb forms so I fumble for my phone and see a message waiting for me in my inbox – up pops 'I want you more and more'. I need to get home and sort this once and for all.

MARK. It's a street that curves and dips, with trees and cats and dog shit in amongst the leaves and I'm playing a sort of hopscotch with my feet as my heart dances next to all my organs and the fingertips on my left hand go numb.

JOHN. 'I'm afraid that's time up, so nice to meet you Mrs, Miss Taylor, I really do think Mark should keep up with the running, exercise is good for the mind after all' and no, wanking doesn't count.

MARK. I have a quick rub of my crotch just to make sure it's up and ready – can't believe this is actually happening.

Check my phone, I have fifty-five minutes till I need to be back at home, and sex only usually lasts like twenty minutes unless it's a really long porn movie.

JOHN. Year Eleven done, the Head steps up and I do that awkward half-run to the back of the hall. I can get home in six minutes if I drive fast, have a bit of a row, break up with Claire, get her to beg for me back which I will accept and then it's over and we'll be... happy finally. I will meet Tim. I will meet this man I have been, well, sort of cyber-shagging.

MARK. I am Tim and Tim is a dude, with a massive dick. 24, Flat 24, buzzer B, the middle flat. I press the bell.

JOHN. I get in the car where I see Mrs Taylor having a lonely fag by the school bins, Christ not even Mr Murphy would fuck her and he's a fan of a minger.

MARK. I hear her voice, Claire's voice, 'coming' she calls to me as she stumbles down the stairs, I can see her shadow approaching through frosted glass but I can't quite –

JOHN. – see how we got here, me and Claire, things have been alright, not great but okay, I think I really meant it when I told her I loved her –

MARK. – face looks distracted as she lets me in, she doesn't fall into my arms, or answer the door wearing nothing but suspenders and bra, I'm a bit confused, disappointed? What does it matter at least I'm in –

JOHN. – to our street and I can see a guy going into the main door and he's shorter than I thought Tim would be but I can't make him out as the rain hits my windscreen, is that Claire –

MARK. – muttering about internet providers and broadband deals, we climb the stairs till we stop at the front door of her flat, I see and smell cats, home, a full bin, a wooden floor, pasta in jars and open bottles of wine. Then she turns and looks me in the eyes for the first time and stops.

JOHN. I park the car and a good song comes on the radio and it's like I'm in a movie, a fucking James Bond wannabe. Smacking rain hits the pavement and it's that thing – what do

you call it? 'Pathetic fallacy', is it bad that I'm this excited –
how long has it been since I've punched someone? What was
it Dad used to say – 'up and through, son, or just kick 'em
and run'. Finally I'm going to see Tim, find out what's so
much better about him.

MARK. 'You're a bit young' she says, 'where's your badge,
your uniform?'

Shit how does she know I'm a schoolboy – has she known
all along?

'It's at home' I say, 'I thought I'd look nice for you, you
know – I didn't really know what to wear actually.'

Looking at me now like I'm mental, confused dot com you
can see her mind practically whirring.

'Sorry but who are you?'

JOHN. Waiting in the car letting the windows steam up, write
'Tim' in the condensation and then a massive spunking cock
just dripping semen all over his shit name over and over
again. Start rubbing it out so hard I almost punch the glass.

MARK. 'I'm Tim, Tim Walker'… rhymes with stalker…

'I'm Tim.'

'From BT?' she asks.

'From, from Lloyds Bank.'

'What?'

'From Milton Prep and Secondary School.'

'Right, one of John's pupils, Mr Martin's pupils.'

John, she called him John and when she said it she smiled.
She didn't know the name Tim. Her eyes didn't recognise his
name and it feels like I'm slipping down a very hot hole of
embarrassment because this isn't how it's meant to be.

'Why have you come round, Tim? He's not here, he's at
parent-teacher evening'

JOHN. Finally stopped dicking about and I'm at the main door
to the flat and I'm getting the keys out that slip through my
fingers as I get soaked, and I think it must be the excitement
because my hands are shaking.

MARK.There's a fumble at the door and we both look down
and for some reason that's when I feel a stranger at my neck
and back and I don't think I just act – I walk forward and she
steps back, one bit of loose slipper-sock thing and she trips
on the newly mopped, extra-shiny, extra-Ikea wooden floor
and hits her head with a fucking thwack.

She hasn't opened her eyes for a while, I don't think I can do
mouth-to-mouth and I don't know any first aid, but I notice
that seconds are slipping by like a really dull Sunday so
maybe it hasn't been that long just that time's gone warped. I
think the flat seems to be shaking but I realise it's my body
that's trembling.

I get water, yeah cold water and I splash it in her face but
she's still not moving.

I can see her chest pulsing so she's not, dead, what just out
for the count, concussed even? I put my ear close to her face
to see if I can feel or hear her breath and I realise as I do this,
like in that perfume advert I am smelling her neck and her
really nice jawline.

And she smells of this light sweet smell, like posh perfume
and if I smell closer to her armpits it's of I dunno – Dove
deodorant, but her hair smells of coconuts and all together
the mix is so heady but I know from other boys that it's
nothing compared to the smell of down below – a mix of
coins and fish or so I'm told. I've sniffed coins in
preparation, iron and tin and old things – and I'm tempted
right now as the flat is quiet and the situation is strange to
make it stranger and smell Claire's um area.

She's wearing tight light jeans, one of those long cardigan-
type things and I can even see a bit of her belly where her
top doesn't quite meet and it's really white but tough-looking
– like not-quite-cooked chicken. I'm thinking of all the porn

I've seen where the woman is just pretending to be asleep and there's a guy a bit like me, just sort of investigating and it's like she's waiting, expecting to be fucked.

But Claire's not playing, she's not acting, this is a live situation isn't it like in the *Big Brother* house or *Made in Chelsea*. Wait, no you see I'm not so sure any more because nothing about this seems normal or boring instead it does seem like something you would see made up on TV, on the internet, in my dreams, the line of a woman just waiting here for me. I put my hand out and I touch the white bit.

Her skin is so soft but goose-pimply she must be cold, and I think she should probably wake up now but she looks so asleep and this must be the face that Mr Martin wakes up to every morning and how lucky is that? I think about my shit little bed at home that sags at the edges and smells of really old cum and socks and I just want this to be the next bit in my life, to be clean in fresh sheets with Claire looking at me with the same smile in her eyes when she said his name, and I don't know why but I see my dad grinning at me winning all of the heats, the nationals and the championships and know that I have experienced love and tenderness and I begin to cry like I haven't in a really long time. I really just want her to wake up now, so I put my body on top of hers, lift her up and keep her warm and just hold her.

She starts to open her eyes blearily, all out of focus like a druggie and I think 'thank fuck she's okay', why am I here with this woman, have I even hurt her? I need to leave now that she's alright, just get out and far away and into my bed and stay there, not play this game any more. I put her gently back down and head for the door.

JOHN. 'Mark.'

MARK. 'Mr Martin.'

And now I see what the situation appears to be or is really, me standing over his dead-looking girlfriend, face smudged and wet from my face on hers – it looks a bit fucking suspicious.

JOHN. It's not Tim, it is not Tim, it is Mark shitty Taylor, one of my shit-for-brains pupils and yet here in my flat, close to my Claire who's just – what the fuck has he done to her? It's clicking then and I'm figuring the ballbag out because he's Tim, must be, on Facebook, how easy can that be – so what, wait and he thinks, and she's not, because she's me, I've… what… okay, okay, John, let's be clever about this one. He's looking right at me the spotty cunt and I almost want to laugh and tell him it's alright – but it isn't – 'Claire.'

MARK. He tells me to call an ambulance how long has she been like this for, what have I done to her?

'Nothing honest, Mr Martin, she slipped on the floor, I…'

JOHN. 'You better call the police and all.'

MARK. 'No wait please, I'm sorry I can't, I promise I didn't hurt her it all just happened.'

'Why are you here, Mr Martin?'

JOHN. 'Why the fuck are you?' And I want to say 'Tim', to let his little pea-shaped brain have a chance of knowing what's really happened, but fuck that, be locked up as a paedo for sending those messages, those photos. Shit what if Claire ever knows.

MARK. He calls the ambulance because my fingers can't, she's moaning about her head on the floor and he's there next to her smoothing her hair, telling her it's okay, and I thought that's what Tim would say, but now she's proper coming round and I've got to get out.

JOHN. 'Flat 24B Colby Road please, wait, Mark no, shit sorry just come yeah it's my girlfriend please.'

MARK. I run, I run down the stairs, past the front door, through the gate, up the street, forgetting to step carefully over dog-poo leaves and plastic bags, just keep ploughing through and through and don't go back and save her, because I'm the one she needs saving from.

JOHN. I'm alone in the flat with Claire, her head in my lap and as she struggles to collect herself, pull herself up and back into the world, I can't seem to help her, because for a minute everything is perfect, we are here together and there's no anger, pain, resentment, there's just us – and in a way I sort of don't want her to ever wake up.

MARK. And run and run and run and run and it feels clean out here like there's too much air and my face bursts with it and the tears keep falling till I can't see, that was not what it was supposed to be and what does this make me – did I do something bad? I don't know any more what I'm supposed to do, I thought I was getting it right but I think I just got lost for a second, I just got lost. I need to get away from that place. I need to get away from him.

She didn't know me, she didn't know Tim.

JOHN. The paramedics come, 'oof you've had a nasty bump to the head', the young one eyes me up like I'm an abusive boyfriend, like 'we've seen this before and don't think we don't know' yeah, yeah.

I can't be bothered, mate, stare back at her till her doe eyes do a blink and think better of it – say something if you really thought it.

'No blood from her ears and no pupil bigger than the other, still you were out cold for how long?' 'Five to six minutes', they decide to take her in for observation. She looks at me panicked then – 'I'll meet you there' I say. Then they take her away, and I feel a bit... relieved.

MARK. I get home and she's already there, I can't look her in the eyes.

'You did okay' Mum says, 'in fact maybe we should go out for dinner and celebrate'.

'I've been out running', but she sees the mess of my face and knows that it's more than that, my tear stains embarrass her I think, they embarrass me.

'You look like shit' Shannon says.

'Why are you wearing your good shirt?'

'He went out, Mum.'

'You didn't put the tea on.'

I run upstairs before they see into my brain and know what's happened, till I start blubbering on the floor and telling them everything. So I do as usual, I slam and lock the door and then I log on and look at it all, the photos, the messages, the bits I copied and pasted and it's like a big thick cloud opens up around my room with her all over it, her face and her eyes, and her neck and her thighs, and the top-ten chat-up lines, the paedos in Malta, the kids with their hands on the things they shouldn't be touching, the women on the other end of the line, the live chat-up lines, the webcam sex and the torture porn, the revenge sites and the fetish pages and the slap a bitch fight 'em and tie 'em up games and the fucked-up faces of the teenage websites and the Return of Kings and the Lad Bible and the fuck the bitch till she dies YouTube sites and the comments and the likes and the trolling and the nothing is barred because it all comes from our minds.

She didn't want some shitty little teenage boy in her house let alone her bed, she didn't know you, Mark, she didn't know Tim so it was all in my head, like a sick little stupid piece of shit in budget trainers swapping shag fantasies with a woman so out of your fucking league. I delete all of it.

I delete Tim.

He's gone and I stare at myself in the empty computer screen and switch it off.

JOHN. The flat is empty, and my body starts shaking because of all the adrenalin, I get a beer out of the fridge but I spill most of it on the floor – just a puddle of gold liquid that I ignore. She didn't know Tim, he wasn't Tim, Tim has never existed, there's been only him. Somehow I'm now on the floor and I'm trying to piece together where it all went wrong. I should go and look after her but I wake up hours later to her mum calling me, telling me not to bother showing up she's taken her back to theirs. She won't be coming back to our flat for some time, it's no longer hers and mine.

Right.

No.

Does she think all of this is my fault?

I get my laptop out and stare at Tim's emails, I'm about to delete them, my account, my messages, the photos, but I keep them instead and I just keep looking.

MARK. When Dad died he had this shit blog he was really proud of – before Tumblr was even a thing and you would've thought he has just invented space travel cos he was beaming for days, going upstairs to put another post on – 'gotta keep my views up, son', and he would look at me like 'see we understand each other' but I told him that no fucker in their right mind wanted to know about middle-aged running clubs and he said 'that's where you're wrong, son, that's where you are so very wrong'. He would say that a lot and try not to let me get to him, because for some reason I used to like to undermine him even though I loved him.

When he signed up for the London Marathon he linked it to his JustGiving page and it was like he had landed on the moon.

Mum said it was unfair that a man that fit should just drop down dead and her friend said – 'it's always the ones you least suspect'. And I told her to go fuck herself in my head but not out loud because everyone looks at you really hard when it's your father's funeral.

Shannon did a lot of fainting which was annoying, and Mum kept holding my hand saying 'thank you for keeping it together – we need you to keep us all together' and so I decided I wasn't going to be what they needed.

Online there are people who create Facebook pages for dead people, loved ones, relatives, pets. My mum wanted me to

make a page on his blog to tell people what had happened –
'they need to know' she said, 'they're not pen pals, Mum,
that's not how it works, they'll just think he gave up
blogging for a bit' and I rolled my eyes at her for a full stop.

Sometimes I did check it, just to see if he'd had any more
views, but then I realised I was the one making the counter
go up.

JOHN. I spend the weekend packing up the flat, we've arranged
a time for me to be out so she can collect all of her things –
which is almost well… everything, and I found a bag under
the bed, already packed with some of her stuff like she could
have gone at any moment. I look up who I can ask for help
on Facebook, surely I've got an old mate with a spare room
for when we give back this place, and I realise all of our
friends are not mine, but Claire's, again.

I think I might stay with Mr Murphy but the idea of sleeping
on his leather sofa, and its squeaky far-too-sad surface is
enough to make me gag a bit, so I stay put in an empty flat,
just me, myself and the TV.

I use this time to go online, on my phone, on my laptop, my
iPad and I look at everything that everyone looks at.

See flashes of them fucking on our bed.

I sit and it's silent because the hum of the online world
barely touches the sides, and when I sleep on the bed, it
smells of her so I crawl up onto her side.

Anna doesn't call me back all weekend and I think she might
have finally gone and got herself a 'proper boyfriend', good
luck with that. I give up trying to get in touch with Claire,
she's not replying to anything I send her, she appears to be
'single' on her profile, which gets lots of 'likes', nice. I try
her parents but there's no one there 'apparently' and it looks
like this is the way it's going to be and I've got no one else
to blame for once.

MARK. Today is a normal day, except I don't think it ever will
be – I have French first thing and I'm thinking 'can I just

never turn up ever again' but no, Mark, because if anything there's a bit of me that wants to stop running away from things that are hard and scary. I put my school tie on and make sure to say hello to Mum this morning – I'm trying, Dad, you see, I can make things better trust me – and he looks up at me from my iPhone screen.

JOHN. Then it's Monday and I'm dragging myself to school. It's French first thing and I'm thinking 'can I just fake having the shits and get someone to cover me' – but fuck that I'm not letting a teenager beat me. I pull myself together just in time to greet Mr Murphy, don't tell him about Claire, don't tell him about anything. I'm not having a sad sack like him pity me.

MARK. I see him just a bit ahead of me – no tie between us any more, I cross over to the other side of the street. But I still watch him – feel the urge to ask him what he thinks. Does he know I'm Tim, has she told him everything?

JOHN. I look around to spot him, see if he's had the guts to turn up – and he's there – just behind me, like he's a really shit shadow that I don't want to be tied to. His presence unnerves me because if he knows it was me, and he tells anyone anything I'm fucked for life, so I know what I have to do to keep him quiet.

MARK. In French he barely looks at me, I don't put my hand up and try to be funny. I just look at the page ahead of me and do the exercise about Dominique who fucking loves the library.

Ashleigh and Rob sit apart from me – 'think you're too cool for us now or somfing' Rob has texted – 'let's go paintballing this Sunday' I reply 'safe one mate'.

JOHN. Can you stay behind please, Mark?

MARK. Yes, Mr Martin.

JOHN. Mark, I think we should /

MARK. / I am so, so sorry, Mr Martin, is she okay, is she hurt or anything /

JOHN. / Claire's fine, Mark, a bump to the head but she's um, she's fine.

I just wondered how much you said to one another, what you spoke about in the flat?

MARK. Nothing, sir, honest I, it was all just a big...

JOHN. ...Misunderstanding right, I thought...

MARK. Sorry yeah it all just got a bit, sir I –

I... will you tell her how sorry I am –

That I won't do anything like that ever again

I won't /

JOHN. / It's fine, Mark, I think we can just put a line under it maybe.

Just let this be between you and me.

MARK. Course, sir.

JOHN. When did your dad die, Mark?

MARK. Summer holidays, sir.

JOHN. I'm really sorry to hear that, Mark, mine died, um Jesus um seven years ago, on Christmas Day actually – which was annoying, really pissed my mum off, she just chucked everything away, turkey, tree, lights, you can imagine.

MARK. Yeah my mum refuses to throw any of it away.

JOHN. People react differently I suppose.

At one point though I think you have to let those people go, so you don't go on pretending that you're someone else, you know. I get it I think, is what I'm trying to say.

MARK. Right, sir, I think I can be better, I want to be better.

...

I think I should go to Chemistry, going to be /

JOHN. / Yeah, yeah course just before you go –

Why Tim?

MARK....

Because of you, sir.

Pause.

My history is blank I can start again, better this time, 'come on, son', 'coming, Dad.' I put my pyjama bottoms on, an old PE top and slip down the stairs, I get a tray and put three glasses of Robinsons on it and a glass of Shloer for Mum, one ice cube, just how she likes it.

JOHN. That night I am in the flat alone again, with only my laptop and the TV, my regular company. My search history is full of all things Tim, messages, pictures, things I wanted to send him, and my future is nothing but class after class of teenagers whilst I stay on the same page in the same textbook. It feels faintly fucking meaningless.

MARK. I take one to Aaron in bed and think I'll let him win a game tomorrow – maybe.

I take the rest into the living room, put the tray down on the coffee table and let Shannon stay on the best cushion.

JOHN. I try to see if Claire is online again, she's un-friended me and changed her privacy settings – suppose that's a good thing considering...

I call her again but it seems she's changed her number – which must have been a nightmare, or maybe her phone was stolen or she's ignoring me which is the truth isn't it really. Keep looking over to the kitchen floor – just see Claire lying there.

I wish I had kept her there.

MARK. We don't say anything, we just keep on looking at the TV screen, but my mum is smiling through her shoulders and Shannon's foot rests next to mine and we are happy for the first time in ages.

'I miss Dad' I say. And I feel relieved just to admit it.

JOHN. So I create a profile, a new one, or an old one I suppose.

I am Tim, I am twenty-eight, I work at Lloyds Bank, like pictures of funny cats, tae kwon do and *Breaking Bad*. I scroll through Google Images creating myself one very good life, posh cars, nights out, Ibiza beaches, festivals and French foods, luxury apartment, posh shoes, gold watches and parents that I can be proud of. I don't know why I do any of this; I do it because I can. Then I add Claire, and I wait for her to accept request.

End.

A Nick Hern Book

WINK first published in Great Britain as a paperback original in 2015 by
Nick Hern Books Limited, The Glasshouse, 49a Goldhawk Road, London
W12 8QP, in association with Theatre503 and Tara Finney Productions

WINK copyright © 2015 Phoebe Eclair-Powell

Phoebe Eclair-Powell has asserted her right to be identified as the author of this
work

Cover image: Adam Loxley

Designed and typeset by Nick Hern Books, London
Printed and bound in Great Britain by Mimeo Ltd, Huntingdon, Cambridgeshire
PE29 6XX

A CIP catalogue record for this book is available from the British Library

ISBN   978 1 84842 482 1